IMAGINE THAT

Licensed exclusively to Imagine That Publishing Ltd
Tide Mill Way, Woodbridge, Suffolk, IP12 1AP, UK
www.imaginethat.com
Copyright © 2021 Imagine That Group Ltd
All rights reserved
2 4 6 8 9 7 5 3 1
Manufactured in China

Written by Eilidh Rose
Illustrated by Ben Mantle

ISBN 978-1-78958-613-8

A catalogue record for this book is available from the British Library

The Christmas Nativity Tale

Written by Eilidh Rose

Illustrated by Ben Mantle

Long, long ago, in a town called Nazareth, a woman called Mary was visited by an angel. The angel told Mary that she had been chosen to have a very special baby – the son of God. 'You will call him Jesus,' the angel said.

Later that year, the Emperor announced that there would be a census and everyone in the land must return to their place of birth, to be counted. So Mary and her husband Joseph had to travel from Nazareth to Bethlehem.

The journey was very long and tiring and Mary was going to have her baby very soon. Mary travelled most of the journey on a donkey, led by Joseph.

Far away, three wise men were studying the night sky when they spotted a new, bright star.

The wise men had been waiting a long time for this sign. They knew that it meant a very special baby was going to be born.

So, the wise men set out on a great journey to follow the star.

When Mary and Joseph arrived in Bethlehem, they tried to find somewhere to stay, but all the inns were full of people who had returned to be counted.

Finally, they reached the last inn in the town. The innkeeper told them the same as everybody else: 'I'm sorry, there's no room here.'

Mary and Joseph were very upset as they had nowhere for Mary to have her baby. The kind innkeeper told them that although he had no spare rooms, they could stay in his stable with the animals.

That night, in the cosy stable, Mary gave birth to baby Jesus. Mary and Joseph wrapped him in a blanket and placed him in a manger filled with straw, as they had no crib.

On a faraway hillside, three shepherds
were looking after their sheep.
Suddenly, a burst of light filled the sky
and an angel appeared, telling them that
a very special baby had been born,
and that he was the son of God.

So, the shepherds began their
journey to Bethlehem
to see the baby.

The three wise men arrived at the stable after the shepherds. When they saw Jesus, they knew that he would be a leader of men, the King of Kings. They gave him gifts of gold, frankincense and myrrh, and knelt to worship him.

Everyone was overjoyed at the birth of Jesus. When the shepherds went on their way, they spread the wonderful news about this very special baby – the son of God and the saviour of the world.

To this day, every year,
we celebrate the birth of Jesus at Christmas.